D1303640

Here's all the great literature in this grade level of *Celebrate Reading!*

Finding a Starting Point

Big Books & Little Books

It's a Perfect Day!
by Abigail Pizer
✳ CHILDREN'S CHOICE AUTHOR

Peanut Butter and Jelly
Illustrations by
Nadine Bernard Westcott
✳ CHILDREN'S CHOICE ILLUSTRATOR

The Gunnywolf
retold and illustrated
by A. Delaney
✳ CHILDREN'S CHOICE

So Can I
by Allan Ahlberg
✳ CHILDREN'S BOOK AWARD AUTHOR

One Gorilla
by Atsuko Morozumi
✳ *NEW YORK TIMES* BEST ILLUSTRATED

Mary Had a Little Lamb
by Sarah Josepha Hale
Photographs by
Bruce McMillan
✳ ALA NOTABLE ILLUSTRATOR

Featured Poet

David McCord

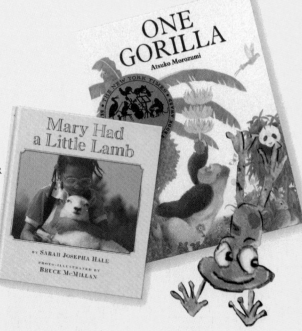

BOOK B

Hurry, Furry Feet

"PARDON?" SAID THE GIRAFFE

Colin West

BOOK C

Our Singing Planet

No Puppies Today!
by Joanna Cole
Illustrated by Brian Karas

Featured Poets

N. M. Bodecker
Rowena Bennett
Mary Ann Hoberman
Lee Bennett Hopkins

Big Book & Little Book

BOOK D

My Favorite Foodles

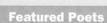

Featured Poets

Eve Merriam
Lucia and James L. Hymes, Jr.
Dennis Lee
John Ciardi
Charlotte Zolotow

Big Book & Little Book

BOOK E

Happy Faces

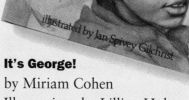

Featured Poets

Big Book & Little Book

BOOK F
A Canary with Hiccups

Featured Poets

Jack Prelutsky
Lee Bennett Hopkins
Shel Silverstein
Gail Kredenser
Zheyna Gay

Big Book & Little Book

Celebrate Reading!
Big Book Bonus

Hurry, Furry Feet

About the Cover Artist
Susan Magurn lives near the ocean in Massachusetts,
where she can often be found rollerblading or biking. She
enjoys illustrating children's books and teaching art to
urban teenagers.

ISBN 0-673-81122-0

1997
Scott, Foresman and Company, Glenview, Illinois
All Rights Reserved.
Printed in the United States of America.

This publication is protected by Copyright and permission
should be obtained from the publisher prior to any
prohibited reproduction, storage in a retrieval system,
or transmission in any form or by any means, electronic,
mechanical, photocopying, recording, or otherwise.
For information regarding permission, write
Scott, Foresman and Company, 1900 East Lake Avenue,
Glenview, Illinois 60025.

CELEBRATE READING! ® is a registered trademark
of Scott, Foresman and Company.

Acknowledgments appear on page 128.

12345678910DR010099989796

Hurry, Furry Feet

ScottForesman

A Division of HarperCollins*Publishers*

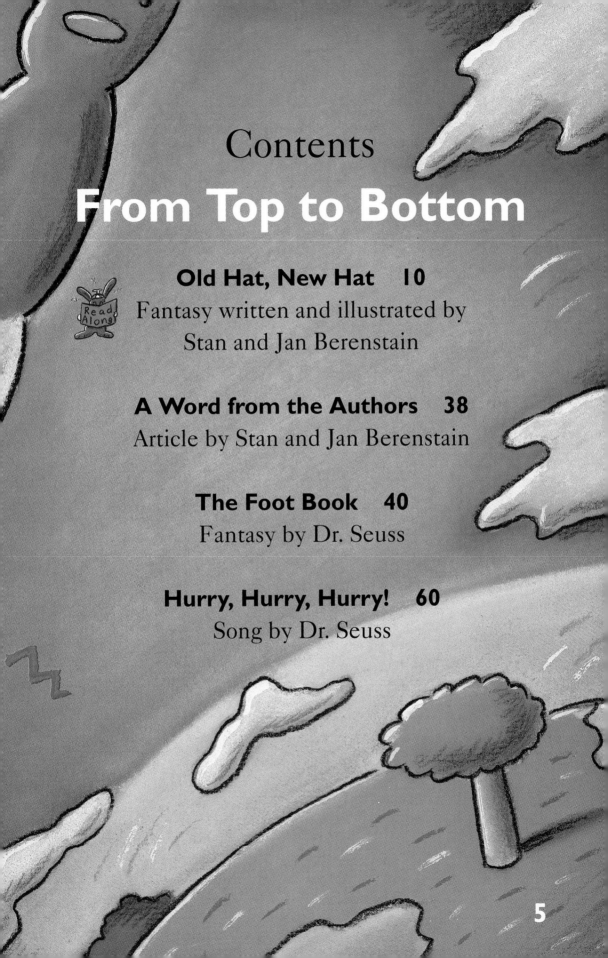

Contents

From Top to Bottom

On the Move

From Top to Bottom

OLD HAT

NEW HAT

by
Stan
and Jan
Berenstain

Old hat.

Old hat.

New hat.

New hat

New hat

New hat

New hat

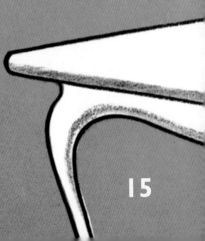

Too big.

Too small.

Too flat.

Too tall.

Too loose.

Too tight.

Too heavy.

Too light.

Too red.   Too dotty.

22

Too blue.   Too spotty.

23

Too fancy.

Too frilly.

Too shiny.

Too silly.

Too
beady.

Too
bumpy.

Too
leafy.

Too
lumpy.

Too
twisty.

Too
twirly.

Too
wrinkly.

Too
curly.

27

Too
holey.

Too
patchy.

28

Too
feathery.

Too
scratchy.

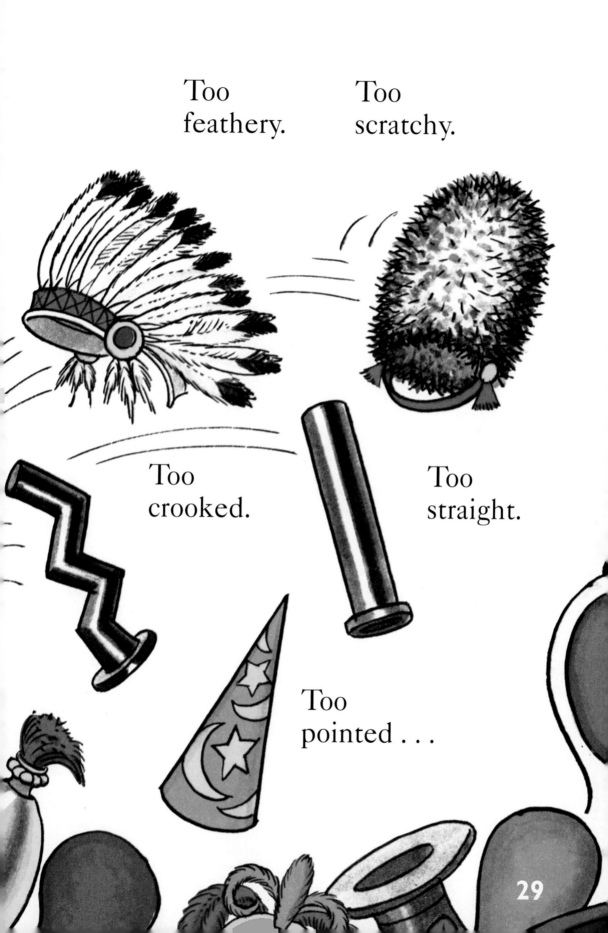

Too
crooked.

Too
straight.

Too
pointed . . .

WAIT!

31

Just right!

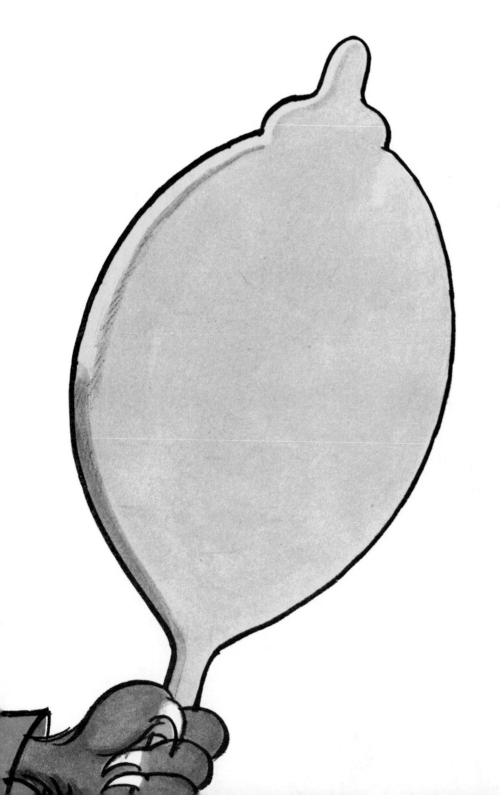

Just right.

Just right.

35

New hat.

Old hat.

OUR BOOK ABOUT HATS

by Stan and Jan Berenstain

We wrote and illustrated
Old Hat, New Hat many years ago when
our two sons were young children.

Both of our sons, Leo and Michael, loved
hats. They had many different kinds of hats.
So we decided to write and illustrate a Bear
book about hats for our sons to enjoy.

Our sons now read Old Hat, New Hat to
their young children, who also love hats.

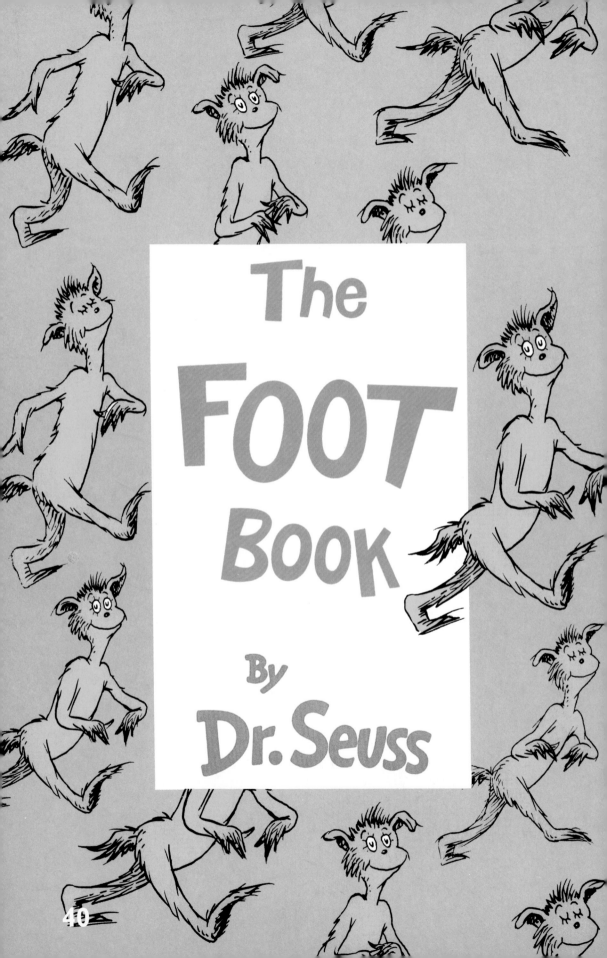

The FOOT BOOK

By Dr. Seuss

Slow feet

Quick feet

Trick feet

Sick feet

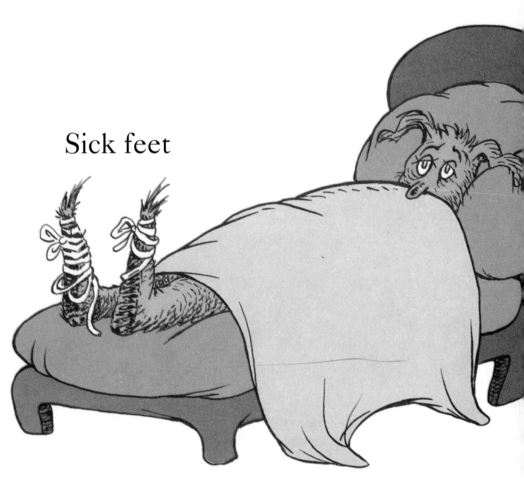

Up feet

Down feet

44

Here come clown feet.

Small feet

Big feet

Here come pig feet.

His feet

Her feet

Fuzzy fur feet

In the house,
and on the street,

how many, many
feet you meet.

51

Up in the air feet

Over a chair feet

More and more feet

Twenty-four feet

55

Here come
more and **more** . . . .

. . . . and **more** feet!

Left foot.   Right foot.

Feet. Feet. Feet.

58

Oh, how many
feet you meet!

Hurry, Hurry, Hurry!

by Dr. Seuss

Two legs, four legs, six legs, eight!
We all have to hurry or we'll all be late.
Hurry, hurry, hurry, or we'll all be late!
Two legs, four legs, six legs, eight!

But when you hurry fast, you begin to puff
and blow.
And your legs won't last, so we'd better
hurry slow.
So let's be late, that's what we'll do,
With our eight legs, six legs, four legs, two!

On the Move

Jump or Jiggle

by Evelyn Beyer

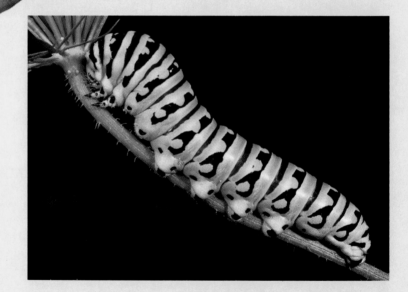

Frogs jump.

Caterpillars hump.

Worms wiggle.
Bugs jiggle.

Rabbits hop.

Horses clop.

Snakes slide.
Sea gulls glide.

67

Mice creep.
Deer leap.

Puppies bounce.
Kittens pounce.

Lions stalk –

but–
I walk!

My Street Begins at My House

by Ella Jenkins

illustrations by James E. Ransome

My street begins at my house.
My street begins at my house.
My street begins at my house.
It's a very special street.

On my street things go up and down.
On my street things go 'round and 'round.
On my street things go upside down.
It's a very special street.

Some streets go one way.
Some streets go two ways.
Some streets lead to the highway.
And some streets go EVERYWHERE.

My street begins at my house.
My street begins at my house.
My street begins at my house.
It's a very special street.

My Street

by Ella Jenkins

When I was a child, I lived on the South
Side of Chicago.

What made **my street** special was: my friends,
the candy store, the shoeshine shop
(they made shoes there), the church across
the street, and the many, many cars, cabs,
and trucks that passed my house each day.

I thought about my special street when I
wrote my song.

If you wrote a song about your street,
what would you write?

Ella L. Jenkins

When the Elephant Walks

by Keiko Kasza

When the Elephant walks . . .

he scares the Bear.

When the Bear runs away . . . .

he scares the Crocodile.

When the Crocodile swims for his life . . .

he scares the Wild Hog.

When the Wild Hog dashes for safety . . .

he scares Mrs. Raccoon.

When Mrs. Raccoon flees with her baby . . .

they scare the little Mouse.

But when the little Mouse scurries in terror . . .

. . .Well, who would be scared by a little Mouse?

A Note from Keiko Kasza

Have you ever been afraid of something?

All of us know how that feels.
That is why I decided to write a story about it.
I wanted children to know that we all get
scared. Even the mighty elephant in my story
is afraid of something!

The next time you feel afraid,
remember there may
be someone bigger
than you who gets
scared too!

Sitting in My Box

by Dee Lillegard

illustrations by Jon Agee

Sitting in my box.

A tall giraffe knocks.

"Let me, let me in."
So I move over.

Sitting in my box.
An old gray
elephant knocks.

"Let me, let me in."
So we both
move over.

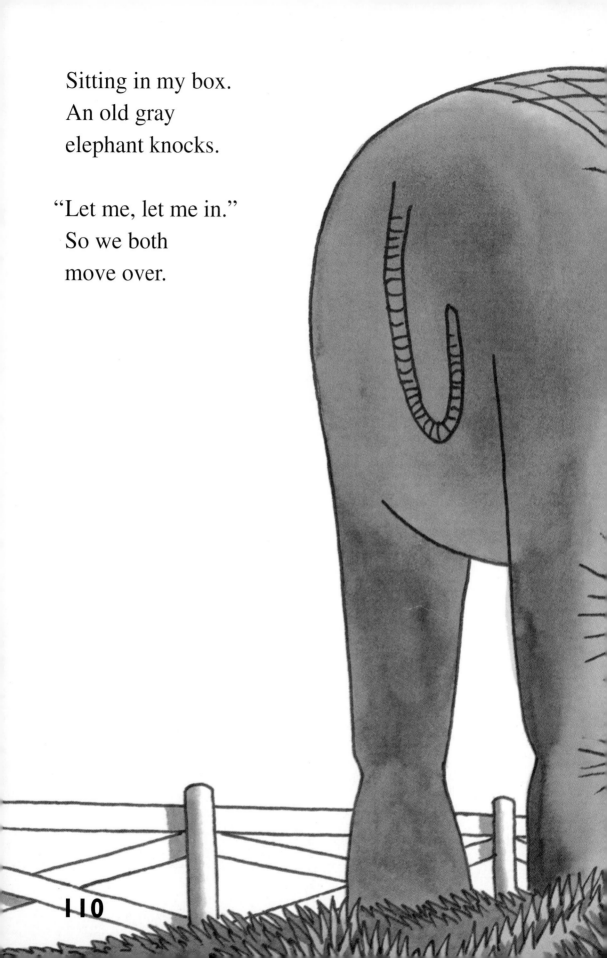

Sitting in my box.
A big baboon knocks.

"Let me, let me in."
So we all move over.

Sitting in my box.
A grumpy lion knocks.

"Let me, let me in."
So we all move over.

Sitting in my box.
A hippopotamus knocks.

"Let me, let me in."
So we *all* move over.

Standing in my box.
There's no room to sit.

"Wait a minute!
This box has
too much in it."

"Someone has to go."

"Not me."

"Not me."

"Not me."

"Not me."

"Not me."

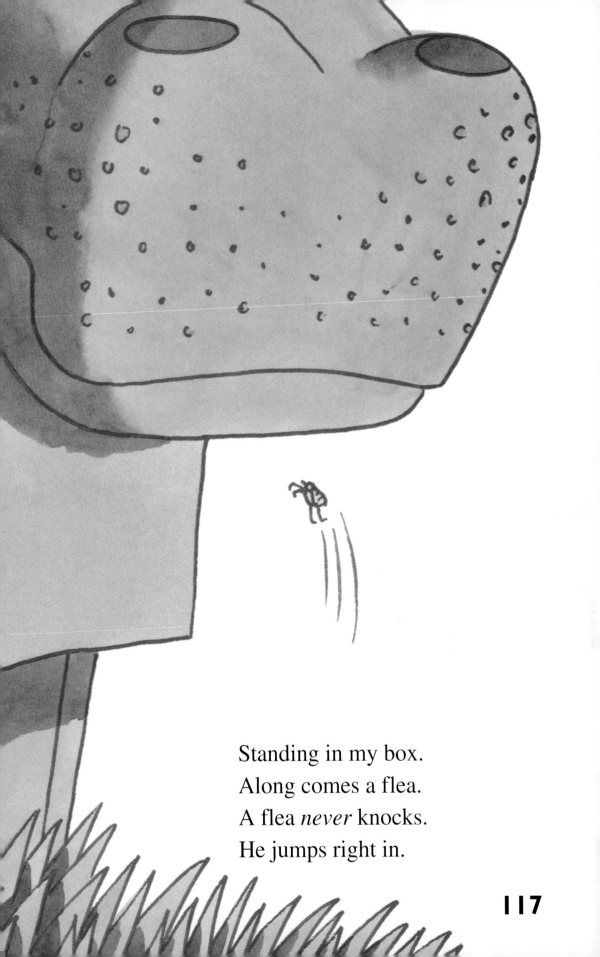

Standing in my box.
Along comes a flea.
A flea *never* knocks.
He jumps right in.

117

He bites the hippo
and the grumpy lion.

He bites the baboon
and the old gray elephant.

He bites the tall giraffe.

That's why I'm
sitting in my box . . .

just me.

Books to Enjoy

Shoes
by Elizabeth Winthrop
Illustrations by William Joyce

There are shoes to skate in and
shoes to skip in. What are the
best shoes for you?

Hooray for Snail!
by John Stadler

Wow! Small Snail hits a baseball
to the moon. Find out if that gives
him enough time to make a home run.

Green Eggs and Ham
by Dr. Seuss

Would you eat green eggs and ham?
Would you eat them on a train? In the
rain? Sam-I-am thinks you'll like them.

Flying
by Donald Crews

Get ready for take-off! See the sights as this airplane flies from the city to the country and back again.

I Walk and Read
by Tana Hoban

This book takes you on a reading walk. You might see some of these signs in your neighborhood.

In the Small, Small Pond
by Denise Fleming

The pond is a busy place before the winter freeze. Read what wiggles, jiggles, flips, or flashes.

Pictionary

Things We Do with Our Feet

jump

kick

skip

dance

march

run

climb

splash

125

Animals

raccoon

camel

bear

crocodile

elephant

hippopotamus

snail

spider

Acknowledgments

Text

Page 10: *Old Hat, New Hat* by Stan and Jan Berenstain. Copyright © 1970 by Stan and Jan Berenstain. Reprinted by permission of Random House, Inc.

Page 38: "Our Book About Hats," by Stan and Jan Berenstain. Copyright © 1991 by Stan and Jan Berenstain.

Page 40: From *The Foot Book* by Dr. Seuss. Copyright © 1968 by Theodor S. Geisel and Audrey S. Geisel. Reprinted by permission of Random House, Inc.

Page 60: The song "Hurry, Hurry, Hurry!" and the illustrations from "The Super-Supper March" were originally published in *The Cat in the Hat Songbook* by Dr. Seuss. Music by Eugene Poddany. Copyright © 1967 by Theodor S. Geisel and Audrey S. Geisel and Eugene Poddany. Reprinted by permission of Random House, Inc.

Page 64: "Jump or Jiggle" by Evelyn Beyer, from *Another Here and Now Story Book* by Lucy Sprague Mitchell. Copyright © 1937 by E. P. Dutton, renewed © 1965 by Lucy Sprague Mitchell. Used by permission of Dutton Children's Books, a division of Penguin Books USA Inc.

Page 72: "My Street Begins at My House" by Ella Jenkins. Words and music by Ella Jenkins. Copyright © 1971 by Ella Jenkins. Reprinted by permission of Ell-Bern Publishing Company.

Page 76: "My Street" by Ella Jenkins. Copyright © 1991 by Ella Jenkins.

Page 78: *When the Elephant Walks,* written and illustrated by Keiko Kasza, copyright © 1990 by Keiko Kasza. Reprinted by permission of G. P. Putnam's Sons.

Page 105: "A Note from Keiko Kasza" by Keiko Kasza. Copyright © 1991 by Keiko Kasza.

Page 106: *Sitting in My Box* by Dee Lillegard. Illustrated by Jon Agee. Text copyright © 1989 by Dee Lillegard. Illustrations copyright © 1989 by Jon Agee. Used by permission of Dutton Children's Books, a division of Penguin Books USA, Inc.

Artists

Illustrations owned and copyrighted by the illustrator.
Susan Magurn, cover, 1–3.
Gary Baseman, 4–9, 62–63, 122–127
Stan and Jan Berenstain, 10–39
Theodor S. Geisel, 40–59, 60–61
James E. Ransome, 72–75
Pam Rossi, (background) 72–76
Keiko Kasza, 78–104
Jon Agee, 106–121

Photographs

Page 38: Courtesy of Stan and Jan Berenstain.
Page 64: (top) Kim Taylor/Bruce Coleman, Inc.
(bottom) Patti Murray/Animals Animals
Page 65: (top) Andrew Rakoczy/Bruce Coleman, Inc.
(bottom) Larry West/Bruce Coleman, Inc.
Page 66: (top) Tom Brakefield/Bruce Coleman, Inc.
(bottom) Fritz Prenzel/Bruce Coleman, Inc.
Page 67: (top) Phil Degginger/Bruce Coleman, Inc.
(bottom) Roger Wilmshurst/Bruce Coleman, Inc.
Page 68: (top) Gary Meslaros/Bruce Coleman, Inc.
(bottom) Charles Palek/Animals Animals
Page 69: (top) Walter Chandoha
(bottom) Bruce McMillan
Page 70: G. Schaller/Bruce Coleman, Inc.
Page 77: Gwendolen Cates
Page 105: Courtesy of Keiko Kasza.